Once upon a time,
a single drop of sunlight
fell from the heavens.

FROM THIS
SMALL DROP OF SUN...

...GREW A **MAGICAL
GOLDEN FLOWER**,
WITH THE POWER
TO HEAL THE SICK
AND INJURIED.

NEARBY, WAS A
GLORIOUS KINGDOM.

THE KINGDOM WAS RULED BY THE MOST GENEROUS KING AND QUEEN, WHO WHERE SOON TO HAVE A BABY.

BUT THE QUEEN BECAME VERY SICK. THE ENTIRE KINGDOM KNEW THE LEGEND OF THE MAGICAL FLOWER AT ONCE, THEY LAUNCHED A SEARCH

THE FLOWER, CENTURIES EARLIER, HAD BEEN DISCOVERED BY A VAIN OLD WOMAN: **MOTHER GOTHEL.**

SHE HOARDED ITS HEALING POWER AND USED IT INSTEAD TO KEEP HER YOUNG.

...FOR A VENGEFUL MOTHER GOTHEL BROKE INTO THE CASTLE, LOOKING FOR THE FLOWER'S MAGIC.

♪♪♪

SHE FOUND IT, BUT SHE ALSO FOUND OUT...

FZAC

...IT WAS IMPOSSIBLE TO SEPARATE THE MAGIC FROM THE BABY!

SO MOTHER GOTHEL STOLE THE CHILD AND VANISHED.

MANY YEARS LATER, IN THE SAME TOWER...

JUST 24 HOURS TILL MY BIRTHDAY! ONE DAY AND I'LL BE 18!

A DAY I GUESS WILL BE SPENT LIKE THE LAST 6 THOUSAND I'VE SEEN... GOOD MORNING, **PASCAL**!

OUT OF THE TOWER?

OH, COME ON, IT'S NOT THAT BAD HERE...

I'LL START WITH THE CHORES! SWEEP, POLISH AND WAX, DO LAUNDRY, DUST, MOP AND SHINE UP... THEN SWEEP AGAIN!

FRUSCH

FRUSCH

THEN I'LL READ A BOOK... OR MAYBE TWO OR THREE.

I'LL ADD A FEW NEW PAINTINGS TO MY GALLERY...

...AND I'LL BRUSH AND BRUSH AND BRUSH MY HAIR. AND THEN... THEN...

...AND THEN, AT DUSK, THE LIGHTS WILL APPEAR, JUST LIKE EVERY BIRTHDAY.

RAPUNZEL! LET DOWN YOUR HAIR!

UH, MOTHER!

AND I'LL KEEP WONDERING WHEN WILL MY LIFE BEGIN? WHEN MOTHER WILL LET ME GO?

OKAY, I'M JUST GONNA DO IT. I'LL ASK HER TO LET ME... LET...

RAPUNZEL! I'M NOT GETTING ANY YOUNGER, DOWN HERE...

"COME ON, PASCAL! DON'T LET HER SEE YOU."

HOW DO YOU MANAGE TO DO THAT EVERYDAY, IT LOOKS ABSOLUTELY EXHAUSTING!

OH, IT'S NOTHIN...

THEN I DON'T KNOW WHY IT TAKES SO LONG.

OH, I'M JUST TEASING. I LOVE YOU SO MUCH! HAHA!

SO, HEM... MOTHER... AS YOU KNOW TOMORROW I'LL TURN 18 AND I... WAS HOPING YOU WOULD TAKE ME TO SEE THE FLOATING LIGHTS!

WHAT?

I NEED TO SEE THEM, MOTHER. AND NOT JUST FROM MY WINDOW... IN PERSON!

GO OUTSIDE? WHY, RAPUNZEL...

NOT FAR FROM THERE...

LOOK AT THIS!

WANTED
DEAD or ALIVE

Flynn Rider
THIEF

IS IT TOO MUCH TO ASK TO GET MY NOSE RIGHT?

THERE!

WANTED
DEAD or ALIVE

THIEF

THERE THEY ARE!

THE ROYAL GUARDS! RUN, GUYS!

OKAY, GIVE ME A BOOST AND THEN I'LL PULL YOU UP.

GIVE US THE SATCHEL FIRST...

WHAT?

I CAN'T BELIEVE THAT AFTER ALL WE'VE BEEN THROUGH TOGETHER...

".YOU DON'T TRUST ME?"

QUICK! THEN HELP US UP!

SORRY, MY HANDS ARE FULL!

WHAT? HOW...?

FLYNN!

DON'T LET HIM GET AWAY!

RETRIEVE THAT SATCHEL AT ANY COST!

FFSSHH

FFSSHH

FFSSHH

FLYNN AND THE HORSE FALL IN THE CANYON BELOW, AND WHEN THEY LAND...

WOW!

THE HORSE IS STILL THERE, STILL SEARCHING FOR HIM...

...SO THERE'S NO CHOICE FOR FLYNN!

ALONE, AT LAST!

PANG

OH, OH... AND NOW?

THUMP

SO RAPUNZEL HIDES THE STRANGER...

OKAY... YOU... STAY... THERE!

I WILL SHOW TO MOM HOW I SORTED HIM OUT... SHE'LL UNDERSTAND I CAN GO OUTSIDE!

AND YOU?

WOW!

...AND WHEN MOTHER GOTHEL RETURNS, RAPUNZEL HAS HIDDEN THE SATCHEL TOO. SHE WANTS TO PROVE SHE CAN GET OFF ON HER OWN, BUT...

I'VE BEEN THINKING ABOUT WHAT YOU SAID EARLIER AND...

I HOPE YOU'RE NOT STILL TALKING ABOUT THE STARS, SWEETHEART.

YOU'RE **NEVER** LEAVING THIS TOWER. **EVER.**

DEEPLY DISAPPOINTED, RAPUNZEL FINDS A NEW WAY TO MAKE HER DREAM COME TRUE...

I... I JUST KNOW WHAT I WANT FOR MY BIRTHDAY, MOTHER. THE PAINT MADE FROM THE WHITE SHELLS YOU ONCE BROUGHT ME.

WELL, IN THAT CASE...

...BUT IT'S A LONG TRIP. 3 DAYS TIME... YOU'LL BE ALRIGHT ON YOUR OWN?

I KNOW I'M SAFE AS LONG AS I'M HERE.

ONCE GOTHEL HAS GONE...

I KNOW WHAT YOU'RE HERE FOR AND... I'M NOT AFRAID OF YOU!

WHAT?

WHO ARE YOU AND HOW DID YOU FIND ME?

OKAY, LET ME ASSURE YOU: I DON'T KNOW YOU, NOR I CAME TO FIND YOU. BUT MAY I JUST SAY...

HI. I'M FLYNN RIDER.

WAIT! WHERE IS MY SATCHEL?

IT'S HIDDEN WHERE YOU'LL NEVER FIND IT! WHAT DO YOU WANT WITH MY HAIR?

THE ONLY THING I WANT TO DO IS GET OUT OF IT! I WAS BEING CHASED, I SAW A TOWER, I CLIMBED IT. END OF STORY.

SO...

YOU COMING, BLONDIE?

I JUST HAVE TO DO IT. SHOULD I? NO...

HERE I GO!

?

...AND THEN...

A MOMENT OF HESITATION, MERE FEET ABOVE THE GROUND...

WOO-HOO! I CAN'T BELIEVE I DID THIS!

NO. WOULD THIS BREAK HER HEART? OF COURSE!

SHE WOULD BE HEARTBROKEN. YOU'RE RIGHT.

I AM, AREN'T I? LET'S GO HOME, I GET BACK MY SATCHEL, YOU GET BACK YOUR MOTHER-DAUGHTER RELATIONSHIP.

NO! NO, I'M SEEING THOSE LANTERNS. AND YOU...

FRRR FRRR

AHH! WHAT IS IT? RUFFIANS? THUGS?

OH... SORRY. I GUESS I AM A BIT JUMPY.

ARE YOU HUNGRY, BLONDIE? I KNOW A GREAT PLACE FOR LUNCH...

MEANWHILE...

SNIFF SNIFF

!

A PALACE HORSE? WHERE IS YOUR... OH, NO...

...RAPUNZEL!

RAPUNZEL! LET DOWN YOUR HAIR!

BUT FOR THE FIRST TIME, NOTHING HAPPENS.

GOTHEL RUNS TO THE BACK OF THE TOWER, TO A SECRET ENTRANCE.

SNAP

SHE BURST THROUGH A HIDDEN DOOR IN THE FLOOR...

RAPUNZEL!

...AND ENTERS AN EMPTY TOWER. **RAPUNZEL IS GONE.**

SHE'S DESPERATE TO FIND OUT WHAT HAPPENED, SO SHE TEARS THE PLACE APART, AND FINALLY UNDER A STAIR-STEP...

?

...THIS IS SOMETHING VERY INTERESTING!

WANTED
DEAD or ALIVE

Flynn Rider
THIEF

!

IN THE MEANTIME...

THE SNUGGLY DUCKLING! A VERY QUAINT PLACE... PERFECT FOR YOU!

GARÇON! YOUR FINEST TABLE, PLEASE!

SLAM

ARE YOU SCARED? MAYBE WE SHOULD GET YOU HOME AND CALL IT A DAY...

O-OKAY...

A PERFECT PLAN TO GET BACK THE SATCHEL, BUT...

WANTED

SLAM

IS THIS YOU?

WANTED! DEAD ALIVE

UGH. NOW THEY'RE JUST BEING MEAN.

HEY! I HAD A DREAM!

DON'T MIND MY EVIL LOOK... I'VE ALWAYS YEARNED TO BE A **PIANIST**!

AND HE'S NOT THE ONLY ONE...

I'M NOT A PRINCE BUT I DREAM OF MAKING A **LOVE CONNECTION**!

I DO **INTERIOR DESIGN**!

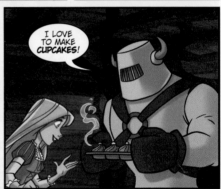

I LOVE TO MAKE **CUPCAKES**!

SO EVERYBODY, WAY DOWN DEEP INSIDE, HAS GOT A DREAM HERE!

THAT'S WHY WHEN THE GUARDS COME IN...

WHERE'S RIDER?

...THE THUGS SHOW HER A **SECRET PASSAGE**!!!

GO LIVE YOUR DREAM...

TOO BAD THAT SOMEONE IS SO DETERMINED TO ARREST FLYNN...

SNIFF SNIFF

A PASSAGE? COME ON, MEN!

...SOMEONE TO TAKE BACK SOMETHING FROM HIM...

LET'S GO GET THE CROWN!

THACK

...AND SOMEONE NOT TO LOSE A TREASURE!

WHERE DOES THAT TUNNEL LET OUT?

?!?

IN THE MEANTIME, INSIDE THE TUNNEL...

WELL, FOR THE RECORD... IT WAS GOOD OF YOU TO STEP IN, THANK YOU.

HMM... SO, FLYNN, WHERE ARE YOU FROM?

WHOA! SORRY, I DON'T DO BACKSTORY.

HOWEVER I AM VERY INTERESTED IN YOURS...

HERE'S MY QUESTION... IF YOU WANT TO SEE THE LANTERNS SO BADLY, WHY HAVEN'T YOU GONE BEFORE?

OH, WELL, I... UHH...

RIDER!

RUN! RUN, RAPUNZEL!

RAPUNZEL, FLYNN AND PASCAL FLEE THROUGH THE UNDERGROUND TUNNELS...

...BUT THEIR PURSUERS ARE EVERYWHERE!

COME ON, BLONDIE!

GRAB

SWISSSH

HURRY, RAPUNZEL!

TAKE MY HAIR!

WOOOH

CRACK

THEN MAXIMUS BREAKS ONE OF THE TANKS' SUPPORT BEAMS AND CATCHES UP WITH THEM...

...AND THE CAVE IS FLOODED!

RRRUMBLE

THE FLOOD CARRIES AWAY EVERYONE AND EVERYTHING...

WOOOOOSH

CRACK

!

SPLASH

CRASH

THEY ARE TRAPPED!

OH, NO...

THUMP

THERE'S NO WAY OUT!

OUCH!

THIS IS ALL MY FAULT. SHE WAS ~~RI~~GHT. I NEVER SHOULD HAVE ~~D~~ONE THIS... I'M SO SORRY, FLYNN.

LASH

A FEW SECONDS LATER...

WE MADE IT! WE'RE ALIVE! PASCAL, WE'RE ALIVE!

THE HAIR ACTUALLY GLOWS. **WHY DOES HER HAIR GLOW?**

EUGENE, IT DOESN'T JUST GLOW...

?

AT THE SAME TIME, AT THE TUNNEL EXIT, GOTHEL WAITS IN VAIN FOR THEM...

THUMP

...BUT WHAT COMES OUT OF THE EXIT IS A USEFUL SURPRISE!

WE'LL KILL THAT RIDER! AND GET BACK THE CROWN!

OR PERHAPS YOU WANT TO STOP AND THINK FOR A MOMENT?

I COULD OFFER YOU SOMETHING WORTH MORE THAN A CROWN... AND IT COMES WITH REVENGE ON FLYNN RIDER.

LATER, IN THE WOODS...

♪ ♫

BUT... YOUR HAIR... HOW DID IT...

I DON'T KNOW. PEOPLE TRIED T[O] TAKE IT ONCE, BUT WHEN IT[...] IT LOSES ITS POWER. THAT[...] MOTHER NEVER LET ME... NEVER...

YOU'VE NEVER LEFT THE TOWER.

SO, EUGENE FITZHERBERT, HUH?

THERE WAS THIS BOOK WHEN I WAS YOUNG. THE TALES OF FLYNNIGAN RIDER!

HE HAD ENOUGH MONEY TO DO ANYTHING, TO GO ANYWHERE! FOR A KID WITH NOTHING... HE WAS A HERO. **MY HERO.**

FOR THE RECORD... I LI[KE] EUGENE FITZHERBERT MU[CH] MORE THAN FLYNN[IGAN] RIDER...

WELL, I... I SHOULD GET SOME MORE FIREWOOD...

BUT ONCE FLYNN'S GONE...

FINALLY! I THOUGHT HE'D NEVER LEAVE.

FRUSH

GASP! MOTHER! HOW... HOW DID YOU FIND ME?

IT WAS EASY. I JUST FOLLOWED THE SOUND OF COMPLETE AND UTTER **BETRAYAL!**

WE'RE GOING HOME, RAPUNZEL. NOW!

YOU DON'T UNDERSTAND. I'VE MET SOMEONE. HE...

...HE LIKES ME.

LIKES YOU? PLEASE, RAPUNZEL! THIS IS WHY HE'S HERE, THE **ONLY** REASON.

GIVE IT TO HIM! GO AND **TEST** HIM... AND YOU'LL SEE.

WILL SHE HAVE THE COURAGE TO TEST EUGENE?

FOR NOW, RAPUNZEL HAS NO ANSWER. FOR NOW, SHE WILL HIDE THE SATCHEL.

THE NEXT MORNING, FLYNN AND RAPUNZEL WAKE UP WITH A BAD SURPRISE...

PLEASE, KNOW THAT I'M OPPOSED TO VIOLENCE!

HEY! EASY, EASY, BOY...

SWIP

YOU'RE A GOOD BOY. AREN'T YOU TIRED FROM CHASING THIS BAD MAN ALL OVER THE PLACE?

LOOK, TODAY IS K OF THE **BIGGEST** OF MY LIFE AND...

...I NEED YOU NOT TO GET HIM ARRESTED. JUST FOR 24 HOURS, OKAY?

IT'S ALSO MY BIRTHDAY, JUST SO YOU KNOW...

DING DONG DING DO

BELL

!

AND THERE IT IS. RAPUNZEL, FOR THE FIRST TIME SEES THE **KINGDOM**.

LATER, A PERFECT DAY BEGINS...

KINGDOM FLAGS!

THANK YOU!

...A DAY OF CELEBRATION IN THE KINGDOM...

...WHERE THE INHABITANTS MAKE RAPUNZEL FEEL AT HOME...

...SHE EXPERIENCES MYSTERIOUS EMOTIONS...

...AND DANCES TO HER HEART'S DELIGHT!

AND WHEN THE SUN GOES DOWN, AND THE MOMENT IS COMING...

WHAT IF IT'S NOT EVERYTHING I DREAMED IT WOULD BE, EUGENE? AND WHAT IF IT IS? WHAT DO I DO THEN?

THAT'S THE GOOD PART, I GUESS...

YOU GET TO FIND A NEW DREAM.

!?

...SUDDENLY THE NIGHT SKY IS FILLED WITH FLYING LANTERNS...

...IT'S ALL RAPUNZEL'S BEEN WAITING FOR...

...HER DREAM COME TRUE.

I HAVE SOMETHING FOR YOU TOO. I SHOULD HAVE GIVEN IT TO YOU BEFORE, BUT I WAS SCARED. AND THE THING IS...

VERYTHING MS PERFECT.

...I'M NOT SCARED ANYMORE. YOU KNOW WHAT I MEAN?

YEAH. YEAH, I DO.

FLYNN SETS THE SATCHEL TO THE SIDE. HE COULD CARE LESS...

BUT, ALL OF A SUDDEN, EVERYTHING GOES WRONG.

THE STABBINGTON BROTHERS!

I'M SORRY, THERE'S SOMETHING I HAVE TO TAKE CARE OF...

IT'S ALRIGHT, PASCAL.

THE CROWN IS ALL YOURS. I'LL MISS IT, BUT I THINK IT'S FOR THE BEST.

THERE.

TINK

WE HEARD YOU FOUND SOMETHIN MUCH MORE VALUABLE THAN A CROWN, RIDER.

WE WANT **HER** INSTEAD.

!

OH, MY PRECIOUS GIRL!

MOTHER?!

I WAS SO WORRIED, SO I FOLLOWED YOU AND I SAW THEM ATTACK YOU AND... ARE YOU ALRIGHT? ARE YOU HURT?

YOU WERE RIGHT, MOTHER. YOU WERE RIGHT ABOUT EVERYTHING...

I KNOW, DARLING. I KNOW.

LOOK! THE **CROWN**!

UH? WHAT? RAPUNZEL? RAPUNZEL?

EVERYTHING IS WRONG. AND MAXIMUS IS THE ONLY ONE WHO CAN DO SOMETHING.

LATER, AT THE KINGDOM PRISON...

LET'S GET THIS OVER WITH, RIDER.

YOU...?!

HOW DID YOU KNOW ABOUT HER? TELL ME, NOW!

IT WASN'T US. IT WAS THE OLD LADY.

OLD LADY?

WAIT! YOU DON'T UNDERSTAND, SHE'S IN TROUBLE!

THE GUARDS LEAD HIM AWAY...

...WHEN SUDDENLY ALL THE DOORS SHUT, TRAPPING THEM!

BAM

WHAT'S THIS?

OPEN UP!

PASSWORD?

WHAT?

NOPE.

THE **TAVERN GUYS!** MAXIMUS TOOK THEM TO SAVE FLYNN AND TAKE HIM TO RAPUNZEL'S TOWER...

...WHERE EVERYTHING IS JUST AS IF NOTHING EVER HAPPENED.

BLUE? OH, COME ON. IT'S NOT THAT BAD.

OR IS IT? RAPUNZEL HOLDS THE FLAG FROM HER DAY IN THE KINGDOM AND LOOKS AT THE CEILING...

SHE LOOKS AT THE FLAG, THEN BACK TO HER PAINTINGS. AND SUDDENLY THE DRAWINGS DISAPPEAR LEAVING ONLY THE SYMBOL OF THE KINGDOM!

AND SHE UNDERSTANDS.

SHE REMEMBERS EVERYTHING. THE KING, THE QUEEN, THE CROWN, THE LOST PRINCESS...

FREEDOM! WITH THE HELP OF HIS NEW FRIENDS, FLYNN RIDES MAXIMUS TO RAPUNZEL'S TOWER...

RAPUNZEL, LET DOWN YOUR HAIR!

...THE HAIR FLOWS TO THE GROUND AND HE CLIMBS IT...

...SUSPECTING NOTHING...

I THOUGHT I'D NEVER SEE YOU AGAIN.

MMPF!

...BUT IT'S TOO LATE!

DON'T WORRY, HANDSOME...

NO! MMMPFT! LET ME SAVE HIM!

AND WHY WOULD I DO THAT, DEAR?

IF YOU LET ME SAVE HIM, I'LL NEVER TRY TO ESCAPE... JUST LET ME HEAL HIM AND YOU AND I WILL BE TOGETHER FOREVER JUST LIKE YOU WANT.

PROMISE!

I... I PROMISE. JUST LET ME HEAL HIM.

EUGENE!

EUGENE! OH NO... I'M SO SORRY. BUT I'LL DO IT, NO MATTER WHAT I'LL SAVE YOU...

NO, DON'T DO THIS.

I'LL BE FINE... IF YOU ARE OK, I'LL BE FINE.

RAPUNZEL, WAIT...

ZACK

OH, NO! EUGENE. DON'T GO, STAY WITH ME. DON'T LEAVE ME.

HEY... YOU WERE MY NEW DREAM.

AND YOU WERE MINE.

RAPUNZEL WEEPS, AS SHE DOES...

...A SINGLE GOLDEN TEAR FALLS FROM HER EYE...

...AND JUST WHEN ALL HOPE SEEMS TO BE GONE...

...RAPUNZEL'S LOVE WORKS PURE MAGIC.

EUGENE!

RAPUNZEL!

"FINALLY, RAPUNZEL RETURNED HOME. THE FAMILY WAS REUNITED."

"THE KINGDOM REJOICED FOR THEIR LOST PRINCESS HAD COME BACK."

"AND SO, ESPECIALLY FOR THE TWO OF US..."

"...DREAMS CAME TRUE ALL OVER THE PLACE."

THE END

RY PUPPY DREAMS OF AN OWNER...

GRRROWL!

...SOMEONE TO SHARE A THOUSAND ADVENTURES WITH...

SNARRL!

SQUEAK

Disney
BOLT

THAT ONE.

YIP! YIP!

YOU'RE HEAVY!

AND **SLOBBERY**! YOU'RE MY GOOD BOY!

FIVE YEARS LATER...

HELLO?

PENNY, I DON'T HAVE MUCH TIME! SOMETHING'S COME UP AT WORK...

...YOU CAN'T GO BACK TO THE HOUSE, PENNY!

DADDY! WHAT'S HAPPENING?

IT'S WHY WE MOST CERTAINLY DO NOT LET THE DOG SEE BOOM MICS!

BECAUSE, MINDY FROM THE NETWORK, IF THE DOG BELIEVES IT, **THE AUDIENCE BELIEVES IT!**

YOUR RATINGS ARE **DOWN** A FULL POINT WITH 18-35-YEAR-OLDS.

SO MAYBE YOU SHOULD SPEND A LITTLE LESS TIME WORRYING ABOUT THE DOG'S METHOD ACTING AND MORE TIME FIGURING OUT HOW TO STOP 20-YEAR-OLDS IN TOPEKA FROM **CHANGING THE CHANNEL!**

SLAM

OR I WILL **FIRE EVERYONE IN THIS ROOM!** HOW'S THAT FOR REAL?

THERE.

YOU SAVED ME AGAIN, BOLT! I'M FINE!

GRRR!

GO GET IT, BOLT!

DON'T WANNA PLAY BALL? WHAT DO WE HAVE HERE? YOUR OLD BUDDY, MR. CARROT!

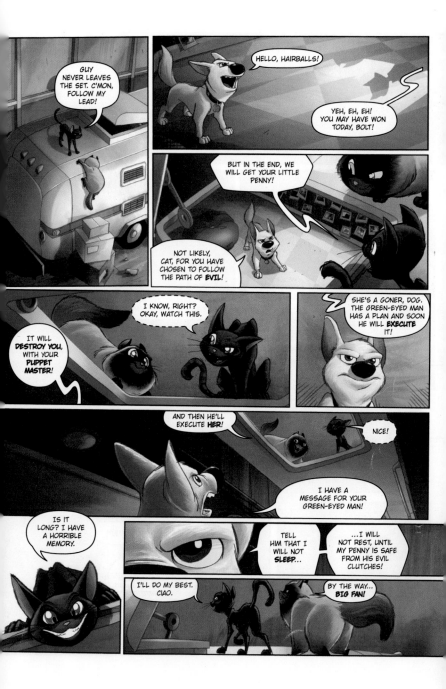

CALICO'S CAPSULE!

I'LL SAVE YOU, PENNY!

BONK

VROOOOOom

LOS ANGELES   NEW YORK

MANY HOURS AND MILES LATER...

HUH?

THUMP THUMP

WHOA!

I'M COMING, PENNY!

?!?

MEANWHILE AT THE STUDIOS...

I'VE GOT GOOD NEWS.

I BOOKED YOU ON THE TONIGHT SHOW! **LEAD GUEST**...

...WHICH MEANS NOTHING IF BOLT IS STILL MISSING.

HE MUST BE SO SCARED.

THIS IS BOLT WE'RE TALKING ABOUT, BABY.

YOU KNOW H CAN'T BE TO FAR AWAY.

Welcome to OHIO

VROOooom

SO, YOU'RE A **"SUPER-DOG"**, HUH?

WHAT'S YOUR BEST SUPER POWER? CAN YOU FLY?

DON'T BE SILLY, I CAN'T FLY.

SO, WHAT POWERS DO YOU HAVE?

I HAVE A **SUPERBARK**

...BUT IT'S CLASSIFIED I CAN'T TALK ABOUT I' SO I SUGGEST YOU PIPE DOWN AND TAKE ME TO PENNY.

...ID FROM ONE RV TO ANOTHER...

WOW!

THUD

YIP! YIP!

AWW!

...AND ANOTHER.

HELLO, PUPPY!

YIP! YIP!

DID YOU COME FOR SOME OF GRANDMA'S BUTTER-BEAN DUMPLINGS?

...6:11 TIME FOR THE WEATHER ON THE ONE'S...

ZAP

IT REALLY DOES HELP AND IT RELEASES...

YOU WAIT RIGHT THERE AND I'LL BE BACK WITH SOME, OKAY?

HEY MAN, THIS TIME WE'LL DO IT MY WAY!

ZAP

RAT RAT TA RAT TA TA TA RAT TA

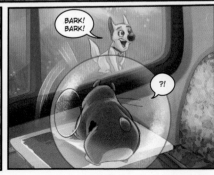

BARK! BARK!

?!

HAVE YOU BEEN OBSERVING ME?

OH, YEAH. I WATCH YOU ALL THE TIME.

THAT'S INCREDIBLE! I'M ALWAYS SO **VIGILANT!**

SO, WHERE'S PENNY?

SHE WAS **KIDNAPPED** BY THE GREEN-EYED MAN!

BUT I'VE CAPTURED THIS CAT!

AN AGENT OF THE GREEN-EYED MAN I PRESUME?

VILE VERMIN! DIE!

EASY, RHINO.

RIGHT. **WE** NEED HER ALIVE.

"WE"?

BOLT, I COULD BE A VALUABLE ADDITION TO YOUR TEAM!

I'M LIGHTNING QUICK! I'M A MASTER OF STEALTH!

WE'RE GOING INTO **THE BELLY OF THE BEAST!**

DANGER AT EVERY TURN!

I EAT DANGER FOR BREAKFAST!

GNNN!

I CAN'T HOLD IT! BOLT!

SNAP

THE THREE ANIMALS FALL OFF THE TRAIN...

...BUT THEY'RE SAFE... MORE OR LESS.

OW!

THE REAL WORLD HURTS, DOESN'T IT?

GET DOWN HERE, CAT!

I'LL GET A LADDER.

YOU'RE PART OF A TV SHOW. YOU'RE NOT REAL!

DO YOU REALLY THINK YOU WERE BORN WITH A MARK IN THE PERFECT SHAPE OF A LIGHTNING BOLT?

IT IS MY MARK OF POWER.

IT IS THE MARK OF A MAKE UP ARTIST!

MITTENS! I'LL SUPERBARK YOU OUT OF THAT TREE!

GO NUTS. LET'S SEE HOW THAT WORKS OUT FOR YOU.

YOU LEAVE ME NO CHOICE! BARK! BARK!

OH, THE SUPERBARK! SCARY! SCARY!

SKREEEK

?! OH, NO! BOLT, BE QUIET!

BARK!

BE QUIET!

HOLD STILL.

COME HERE!

VROOM

AT THE STUDIOS, PENNY IS WORRIED ABOUT WHERE BOLT IS!

LOOK WHO WE FOUND, YOUNG LADY!

JUST LIKE I PROMISED!

BOLT!

THIS IS NOT BOLT!

WELL, THAT DEPENDS ON HOW YOU LOOK AT IT.

IT'S NOT HIM.

LOOK, KID, IT'S TIME WE WERE HONEST WITH YOU.

IF WE DON'T GET BACK INTO PRODUCTION, PEOPLE ARE GOING TO LOSE THEIR JOBS.

GOOD PEOPLE, WITH FAMILIES. WE NEED YOU TO MOVE ON. WE NEED YOU TO LET BOLT GO...

BUT THE "REAL" BOLT DOESN'T WANT TO LET GO...

AAARGHH!

MUST BE MADE OF **PACKING PEANUTS!**

I CAN'T BELIEVE IT! A REAL LIVE SUPERBARK. YOU ARE LEGENDARY!

WE NEED A LIFT! LET'S CLIMB ON BOARD!

IF I DON'T CHASE BAD GUYS, THEN WHAT AM I? I MEAN...

DON'T WORRY ABOUT IT! BEING A DOG IS EASY.

...WHAT DOES A DOG DO?

SLOBBER, SLEEP, CHEW SHOES. IT'S THE GREATEST GIG EVER! YOU KNOW, MOST DOGS LIVE IN A PLACE LIKE THIS, AND...

"...AND, UM, I DON'T KNOW, THEY DO THINGS LIKE..."

WHAT? DRINK OUT OF THIS? BUT.. BUT...

AAH! AND ON COLD NIGHTS, THIS AND A BALL OF YARN!

YOU SEEM TO KNOW A LOT ABOUT THESE PLACES.

LATER, THAT MORNING...

MORNING, CAT. WHERE'S BOLT?

HE'S GONE...

BOLT... LEFT WITHOUT *ME*?

HE WANTED ME TO TELL YOU THAT HE HAD TO FACE THE GREEN-EYED MAN ALONE.

WHERE YOU GOIN'?

TO BOLT. I'VE SEEN IT A MILLION TIMES BEFORE.

THE HERO **MUST GO** AND FACE HIS GREATEST CHALLENGE **ALONE**.

BUT IF BOLT'S TAUGHT ME ANYTHING, IT'S THAT YOU NEVER ABANDON A FRIEND IN A TIME OF NEED.

NO WAY! BOLT!

MEANWHILE, IN CALIFORNIA, BOLT GETS OFF AT HIS STOP...

THUMP

REALLY BIG FANS OF YOURS, BROTHER!

I'M BLAKE, THIS IS MY WRITING PARTNER, TOM, AND BILLY, OUR PERSONAL ASSISTANT.

IF YOU HAVE A SECOND, WE'D LOVE TO PITCH YOU AN **IDEA** FOR YOUR SHOW!

ALIENS. AUDIENCES LOVE ALIENS!

ALIENS?

AH, PROFESSOR. I'D LIKE TO THANK YOU FOR GRANTING US ACCESS TO THAT LABYRINTHINE MIND OF YOURS.

YOU KNOW I'D NEVER DO SUCH A THING, CALICO.

UNLESS IT WAS THE ONLY WAY TO SAVE YOUR LITTLE GIRL'S LIFE!

PENNY!

DADDY!

SMASH

GRRROWL!

GET THAT DOG!

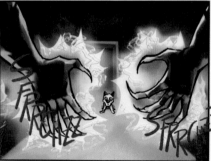

!

♫ TWEET ♫

WHIMPER! WHIMPER!

FIRE! THERE'S FIRE!

CLONK

PHOOM

MEANWHILE, MITTENS HAS FOUND THE REAL BOLT.

BOLT! WHAT ARE YOU DOING HERE? WHY AREN'T YOU IN THERE?

YOU WERE RIGHT, MITTENS. SHE... WASN'T REAL..

NO, BOLT, **YOU** WERE RIGHT. I SAW THE WHOLE THING! SHE'S YOUR PERSON AND...

MITTENS, BE **QUIET**!

WHAT IS IT?

HELP!

"PENNY!"

CLICK

BUMP

YEAH! YOU BETTER RUN!

IS ANYONE STILL IN HERE?

COUGH! I DON'T KNOW!

LOOK! THAT DOOR IS CLOSING!

JUST GET ME INSIDE THAT BUILDING!

I'LL TAKE CARE OF THAT!

IT'S A GOOD DAY TO DIE!

DONG

NOT ON MY WATCH, RODENT!

CRUNCH

CRASH

BARK! BARK!

THE **SUPERBARK!** THE **SUPERBARK!**

OVER HERE! WE'VE FOUND THEM!

SO, THANKS TO BOLT'S COURAGE, PENNY HAS BEEN RESCUED...

SHE'S STABLE. WE'RE GONNA TAKE HER TO THE HOSPITAL JUST TO BE SAFE.

SWEETIE. YOU'RE OKAY. YOU GONNA BE JUST FINE.

BOLT...

...AND AT LAST, SHE AND HER DOG ARE REUNITED.

BOLT HAS NOT BEEN THE ONLY HERO TODAY - MITTENS AND RHINO FOLLOW HIM WITH A TRICK WE KNOW VERY WELL.

CAN'T IMAGINE WHAT YOU MUST BE FEELING.

MY POOR PENNY...

BUT I'M GOING TO MAKE THIS WORK FOR US! I'M TALKING **COVER STORIES! PRODUCTION DEALS...**

WE QUIT.

NO, **WAIT!** LET'S PUT A PIN IN IT!

I'M AFRAID YOUR INJURIES WERE **MORE SEVERE** THAN WE HAD PREVIOUSLY THOUGHT.

WE HAD TO COMPLETELY **RECONSTRUCT YOUR FACE.**

WELL, AT LEAST CALICO WON'T BE ABLE TO **RECOGNIZE ME!**

HEE HEE HEE...

CALICO!

BOLT!

CRASH

THE END.